Core Knowledge Language Arts®

Gods, Giants, and Dwarves

Unit 6 Reader

Skills Strand

GRADE 3

Amplify learning.

Core Knowledge®

Table of Contents
Gods, Giants, and Dwarves
Unit 6 Reader

Introduction to Norse Mythology

Pronunciation Key

Kingdoms of Norse Mythology

Asgard	/o/ /s/	/g/ /ar/		
Valhalla	/v/ /aw/ /l/	/h/ /aw/ /l/	/l/ /ə/	
Jotunheim	/y/ /o/	/t/ /u/ /n/	/h/ /ae/ /m/	
Midgard	/m/ /i/ /d/	/g/ /ar/		
Hel	/h/ /e/ /l/			
Nidavellir	/n/ /i/ /d/	/ae/	/v/ /e/ /l/	/y/ /er/

Who's Who in Norse Mythology

Odin	/oe/	/d/ /i/ /n/	
Frigga	/f/ /r/ /i/	/g/ /a/	
Balder	/b/ /aw/ /l/	/d/ /er/	
Hod	/h/ /o/ /d/		
Valkyries	/v/ /a/ /l/	/k/ /er/	/ee/ /z/
Tyr	/t/ /ie/ /r/		
Freya	/f/ /r/ /ae/	/y/ /ə/	
Sif	/s/ /i/ /f/		
Thor	/th/ /or/		
Loki	/l/ /oe/	/k/ /ee/	
Siguna	/s/ /ee/	/g/ /<u>oo</u>/ /n/	/ə/
Heimdall	/h/ /ae/ /m/	/d/ /aw/ /l/	
Thrym	/th/ /r/ /ie/ /m/		

Kingdoms of Norse Mythology

VALHALLA

ASGARD

JOTUNHEIM

MIDGARD

HEL

NIDAVELLIR

Who's Who in

ODIN

FRIGGA

BALDER

HOD

VALKYRIES

Gods, Giants, and Dwarves

Norse Mythology

THRYM

TYR

FREYA

SIF

THOR

LOKI

SIGUNA

Chapter 1 Sif's Golden Hair

Odin, the father of the Norse gods, sat at the dinner table. By his side sat two **ravens**. Their names were Thought and Memory. They were Odin's flying spies. Each day, they left Asgard, the home of the gods, and flew around the world. Each night, they flew back to Asgard to tell Odin what was happening in the world.

On this day, the **ravens** did not have much to report. Things were quiet on Earth.

Odin tossed the **ravens** some crumbs. He cut off pieces of meat and fed them to two wolves who sat at his feet.

Odin himself did not eat. He never ate. He sipped some **mead** from a goblet. Then, he pushed the goblet away and scanned the room with his one good eye. He spotted two of the Valkyries who worked for him as serving maids. He nodded to them. The Valkyries began to clear the table.

Odin, the father of the Norse gods, was also known as Woden. Many years ago, he Norse people named one of the days of the week for Odin. They called it "Wodensday." Today, we call it Wednesday.

Odin stood up to leave, but just then, he heard a clap of thunder, the snorting of goats, and the skidding of a cart. He knew that could only mean one thing: his son Thor was arriving in his goat-drawn cart.

Sure enough, Thor, the mighty god of thunder, burst into the room. His wife Sif trailed behind him, her head covered with a **veil**. Thor was enraged. The **veins** on his forehead bulged. There was fire in his eyes.

"It's an outrage!" said Thor. "An outrage! This time Loki has gone too far!"

"What's the matter?" Odin asked.

"Her hair!" shouted Thor. "That **scoundrel** has cut off her hair!"

"Whose hair?" Odin asked.

Gods, Giants, and Dwarve

Odin's son Thor was the god of thunder. The Norse people named one of the days of the week "Thor's day." Today, we call it Thursday.

As he said this, Sif let her **veil** fall to her shoulders. Odin looked at Sif and blinked. Her hair—her long, golden hair, which every goddess in Asgard admired—was gone. It had been cut off. There was nothing left but a few tufts of yellow stubble.

"Look at me!" shrieked Sif. "I am **hideous**! I will go live with the **dwarves**! Without my hair, I am as ugly as the ugliest **dwarf**!"

Odin frowned. He turned to Thor and said, "Are you sure it was Loki who did this?"

Odin asked the question, but even as he did so, he felt there was no need to ask. It had to be Loki. It was always Loki. Whenever something was stolen, whenever things went **awry**, whenever any bad deed was done, it was always Loki who was behind it.

"Look at me! I am **hideous** without my hair," shrieked Sif.

Odin blamed himself. It was he who had invited Loki to join the gods in Asgard. Loki was not a god. He was a giant who could change his appearance. Loki had been a constant source of problems ever since.

"I will kill him!" shouted Thor. "I will—"

"Be calm," said Odin. "I will deal with Loki."

Odin called an **assembly** of the gods. He **summoned** Loki as well.

When Loki arrived, he saw the stern look on Odin's face. He saw that Thor was steaming mad, clutching at his hammer, barely holding back his temper. Loki saw that lies would do him no good this time. He knew he would have to admit what he had done. He bowed his head.

"You will restore Sif's hair!" said Odin, in a booming voice. "I know not how it is to be done, but you will do it. I require it of you!"

Loki nodded.

ʌki was not a god. He was giant whom Odin had invited to live at Asgard with ʌe gods.

Chapter 2
Loki and the Dwarves

Loki came up with a plan to replace Sif's hair.

He left Asgard. He went down the Rainbow Bridge to Earth. Then, he went down below Earth to Nidavellir, the **realm** of the dwarves.

The dwarves were short **creatures** who lived deep underground. They were grouchy, **surly**, and unpleasant. However, they were master **craftsmen**. They could make just about anything.

Loki was a smooth talker. He knew how to **flatter** the dwarves. He went to their workshop and watched them work.

"What fine work you do!" Loki said. "Why, I've never seen better **craftsmen**! How do you do it?"

The dwarves smiled. (Who does not like to be praised?)

*ki **flattered** the dwarves.*

Loki went on with his **flattery**.

"You must be the best blacksmiths in the world," he said. "Your work is amazing, but there is only so much blacksmiths can do. I have a task that I fear is too hard even for you."

The dwarves stopped banging on their **anvils** and looked up.

"Too hard for us?" said one of them. "I think not! There is nothing that we cannot make!"

"Could you make golden hair as beautiful and fine as Sif's hair?"

"We can make it!" shouted the dwarves.

Make it they did. They grabbed a bar of gold and heated it in their **forge**. Then, they began banging away at it with their hammers. They stretched the bar into tubes. Then, they stretched the tubes into threads. They beat on the golden threads with tiny hammers until they were as fine as real hair.

Gods, Giants, and Dwarve

The dwarves beat on the golden threads with tiny hammers.

The dwarves worked day and night for a week. When the hair was finished, it was a wonder to behold. It glittered and shone like gold, but it was soft to the touch, like real hair.

Loki had what he needed. He could have gone straight back to Asgard, but he was very clever. He knew he had angered Odin and Thor. He decided to trick the dwarves into making presents for them.

"This hair is amazing!" he said. "You are truly **masters** of your trade. But surely there are some things that even you cannot make."

"There is nothing we cannot make!" said the dwarves.

"Could you make a spear so fine it never misses its target?"

"We can make it!" shouted the sooty, squinty-eyed little men.

*This hair is amazing! Could you make a spear that never misses its target?" asked
oki.*

Make it they did. A week later, the dwarves handed Loki a silver spear. Loki tested it and found that it never missed its target.

"Astonishing!" said Loki. "You are not tradesmen, really. You are artists! But surely there are some things that even the finest artist cannot create."

"There is nothing we cannot make!" said the dwarves.

"Could you make a boat that can sail in the air as well as on the sea—a boat that can be folded up and carried in a pocket?" Loki asked.

"We can make it!" cried the confident little blacksmiths.

Make it they did. A week later, Loki left Nidavellir with the golden hair, the silver spear, and the magical boat.

oki was astonished by the silver spear that the dwarves made.

Loki went up from the underground world of the dwarves. He passed Earth and made his way up the Rainbow Bridge. Heimdall, the **guardian**, saw him and let him pass.

Odin called a meeting of the gods.

Loki placed the golden hair on Sif's head. It was beautiful. Sif was delighted.

Next, Loki gave Odin the silver spear.

Odin was pleased with his present. He convinced himself that Loki was not so bad after all.

Next, Loki gave Thor the magical boat. Thor had never liked Loki. Many times he had longed to pound him to pieces. But even he had to admit that the magic boat was a splendid gift.

So Loki made peace with the gods and all was well in Asgard—at least for the moment.

if, Odin, and Thor were all pleased with the gifts Loki gave them.

Chapter 3 Stolen Thunder

Thor had a hammer that he carried with him everywhere. It was called Mjöllnir [MYOEL-neer].

Mjöllnir was a magical weapon. It had been crafted by the dwarves in their underground workshop. When Thor threw the hammer, it would sail through the air and strike its target. There would be a flash of lightning and a boom of thunder. Then, the hammer would fly back to Thor's hand like a **boomerang**.

Thor loved his hammer. He never went anywhere without it. He even slept with it. The first thing he did when he got up in the morning was grab Mjöllnir.

But one morning, Thor woke up and found that Mjöllnir was gone. He looked everywhere but could not find it.

"Loki!" said Thor. "Loki has stolen my hammer!"

hor looked everywhere for his hammer but could not find it.

Thor found Loki. He took him by the throat and lifted him up so that his legs dangled in the air.

Loki could barely breathe.

"I... did... not... take... it," he stammered.

"Liar!" roared Thor.

Thor glared at Loki and waited for the truth to come out. However, Loki said nothing.

Thor waited a little longer. Still, Loki said nothing.

Thor was puzzled. He began to think maybe Loki was telling the truth this time. (Every so often, Loki did tell the truth.)

Thor set Loki down. He went to speak with Odin.

Odin sent his two ravens out. They flew around the world and came back with a report.

Thor glared at Loki and waited for the truth to come out.

"It was Thrym, the giant," the ravens said. "He stole the hammer."

Thrym was a giant who was quite ugly but very rich.

Odin sent Loki to speak with Thrym.

Loki made the long **journey** to the world of the giants.

Thrym greeted him with a smile.

"Hello, Loki," he said. "How are the gods today?"

"They are not well," said Loki. "Someone has taken Thor's hammer."

"**What a pity**!" said Thrym, but he did not seem too upset.

Loki did not **mince words**. "Was it you?" he asked.

Loki expected Thrym to deny it, but that is not what happened.

din sent Loki to speak with the giant, Thrym.

"Yes!" said Thrym. "I stole the hammer! I have buried it six miles underground, where no one can ever find it! "

Thrym paused briefly to cackle and enjoy his own **villainy**. Then, he spoke again.

"Tell Thor he will never see his hammer again—unless..."

"Unless what?" Loki asked.

"Unless Freya will agree to marry me," said Thrym.

"Not likely," said Loki. "She's married already, you know."

"What do I care?" said Thrym.

"It will never happen," said Loki.

"Then, I will keep Thor's hammer," said Thrym. "No Freya, no hammer!"

hrym said he would return Thor's hammer—but only if Freya would agree to arry him.

Loki went back and told the gods that Thrym had stolen the hammer.

"He says he will give it back, on one condition," Loki reported.

"What is that?" Odin asked.

"If Freya will agree to marry him."

"What?" said Freya. "I will never marry that disgusting **beast**! Never!"

Odin was very wise. He had drunk from the famous Well of **Wisdom**. He had even traded one of his eyes in order to get more **wisdom**. But, even with all this **wisdom**, he was not sure how to get Thor's hammer back.

"What shall we do?" Odin asked the other gods. "How shall we get Thor's hammer back?"

There was a long silence. None of the other gods seemed to know what to do either.

None of the gods seemed to know what to do.

4 A Plan Is Made

The gods sat puzzled. None of them had any idea how to get Thor's hammer back from Thrym.

At last, Loki spoke.

"Perhaps we could trick Thrym," he said.

"Go on," said Odin.

"We can't send the real Freya," Loki said. "That's clear. But maybe we could send a fake Freya."

"A fake Freya?" said Odin. "What do you mean?"

"I mean one of us could dress up as Freya."

"I see," said Odin. "Who did you have in mind?"

"Well," said Loki, with a grin, "it's Thor's hammer. Maybe he should go get it himself."

Well," said Loki, with a grin, "it's Thor's hammer. Maybe he should go get it
imself."

"What?" said Thor. "You want me—the great and mighty Thor—to dress up as a girl? Why, you **rogue**!"

Thor reached out for Loki. He was eager to grab him. Tyr, the god of war, had to hold him back.

"Relax," said Loki. "It will just be for a few hours, until we get your hammer back. I will go with you myself. I will dress up and pretend to be your **maid of honor**."

But Thor was having none of it.

"Never!" he roared. "I will not do it!"

"Well," Loki said, "has anyone else got a better plan?"

Silence.

You want me—the great and mighty Thor—to dress up as a girl? Never!" roared Thor.

At last, Odin's wife, Frigga, spoke.

"Loki's plan just might work," she said. "It's our best chance."

Frigga placed a lovely, white hand on Thor's **massive** shoulder.

"Thor," she said. "I know you don't like the plan, but would you do it for me—and for Freya?"

Thor grumbled and groaned, but in the end he agreed.

"It's just for a few hours," Odin said, patting Thor on the back. "A man can stand anything for a few hours."

The gods sent a message to Thrym. Thrym wrote back. He announced that the wedding would take place in eight days.

Eight days later, the gods were hard at work getting Thor ready.

"Loki's plan just might work," said Frigga.

"Pull!" shouted Frigga.

"I'm pulling as hard as I can!" replied Tyr.

Thor was **barrel-chested** and muscular. It was not easy fitting him into Freya's clothing. Tyr and Loki had already spent ten minutes trying to tighten the waist-strings on Freya's **corset**.

"Why did I let you fools talk me into this?" said Thor.

"Take a deep breath," said Loki.

Thor took a breath. Then, Loki and Tyr began yanking on the **corset** strings.

"It's no use," said Tyr. "We'll never make him look thin and **dainty**."

"You're right," said Loki. "Let's hope he's not too large to fit into Freya's dress!"

Eventually the gods got Thor into his **corset**. They brought him a fancy white dress and **dainty** white shoes.

*'s no use," said Tyr. "We'll never make him look thin and **dainty**."*

They fitted him with veils that covered his face and **concealed** his thick, red beard.

Loki got dressed as well.

Freya came to put on the finishing touch. She took off the famous golden necklace she always wore and placed it around Thor's neck.

At last Thor and Loki were ready. Freya called for her chariot, which was pulled by two cats. Thor and Loki stepped in. The cats mewed and the chariot lurched forward. Thor and Loki were off on their excellent **adventure**.

*e cats mewed and the chariot lurched forward. Thor and Loki were off on their ellent **adventure**.*

Chapter 5 The Wedding Feast

When his wedding arrived, Thrym was as happy as a giant could be.

When he saw Freya's chariot approaching, he felt his heart racing. He had been madly in love with Freya for years. He did not think he would ever get her to marry him. But now it seemed that his dreams were coming true.

"Welcome, fair bride!" he called out.

Thor and Loki stepped out of the chariot.

Thrym came forward. He tried to welcome his bride with a kiss, but Loki pushed him away.

"Not yet!" Loki said, in his most girlish voice. "Not until you are married!"

"Not yet," said Loki in his most girlish voice. "Not until you are married."

Thrym led his guests to a table. They sat down to enjoy the wedding feast.

Thor was hungry. He ate a whole tray of snacks. He ate eight big salmon. He gobbled down half the ox Thrym's servants had roasted. He washed it all down with three barrels of mead. When he was done, he **belched** loudly.

"Urrrrrrp!"

Thrym was taken aback.

"Goodness!" he said. "I have never seen a woman eat so much or **belch** so loudly."

Loki saw the danger.

"Well, you see," Loki explained, "ever since Freya heard she was to marry you, she has been so excited that she has not had a bite to eat—or a drop to drink. For eight days she has **fasted** and thought only of you!"

"Ah," said Thrym. "Well, then it's no surprise she's hungry. Let her eat as much as she wants, the sweet darling! Tell her that her suffering is almost over: she will not have to wait for me much longer!"

Gods, Giants, and Dwarv

*have never seen a woman eat so much or **belch** so loudly!" Thrym exclaimed.*

Thrym sat next to his bride. He tried once more to steal a kiss. He started to lift up her top veil, but quickly dropped it.

"Why do her eyes burn like raging fires?" he asked.

"Oh," said quick-thinking Loki, "that is because she has not slept these past eight nights. She sat up the whole time, thinking of you!"

"Ah," said Thrym. "She is indeed a thoughtful one! I am sorry to have kept you waiting so long, fair one!"

Loki changed the subject.

"Is the wedding present ready?" he asked.

"Yes," said Thrym.

"Perhaps you will go and get it," squeaked Loki.

"I will, indeed," said Thrym.

When Thrym wandered off, Thor growled beneath his veil, "Grrrrrr! I will kill the villain!"

"Hush!" said Loki. "Not until we have the hammer."

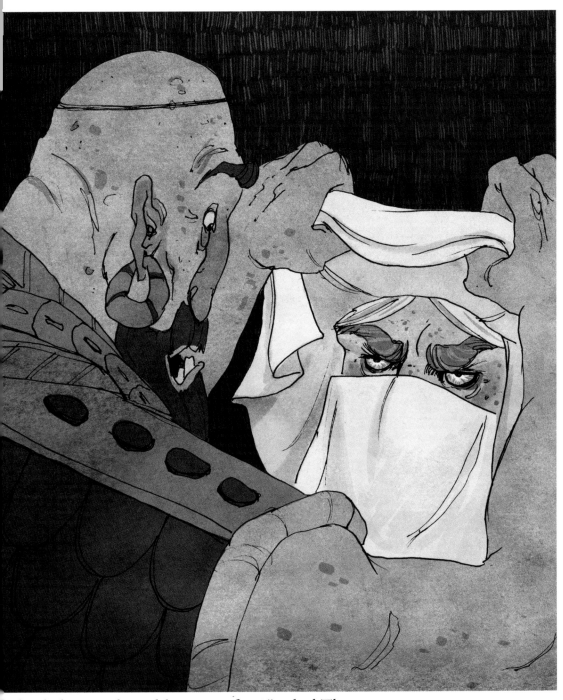

Why do her eyes burn like raging fires?" asked Thrym.

Thrym returned with Thor's hammer. He set it down next to Thor.

"Ooo!" said Thor, in his best girlish voice. "It's so big! May I touch it?"

"If it pleases you, fair one," said Thrym.

"It pleases me," said Thor, still using his girlish voice. Then, lifting the hammer above his head and bursting out of his wedding dress, he called out in a voice like thunder, "IT PLEASES ME GREATLY!"

Boom! Smash! Crash! Thor threw his hammer every which way. Five minutes later, Thrym and all of his servants lay dead on the ground.

Loki and Thor went back to Asgard. There they told their story to the gods. For three days and three nights, the gods ate and drank to celebrate the return of Thor and his hammer.

hor called out in a voice like thunder, "IT PLEASES ME GREATLY!"

Chapter 6

Balder, the Beautiful

Balder, one of the sons of Odin and Frigga, was the god who was most loved. He was beautiful, but he was also kind and friendly. He always had a smile on his face and the other gods smiled when they saw him. Everyone loved Balder—everyone except Loki.

One day, Loki noticed that nobody was paying any attention to him. They were too busy looking at Balder. Loki felt a great hatred welling up inside himself. He began to think about how he might get rid of Balder. He knew it would not be easy, because Balder's mother, Frigga, had gone out of her way to make sure her son was safe.

It had all started many years earlier, when Balder was young. One night Balder had a nightmare. He dreamed of his own death. But the dream was foggy and he could not tell how he died.

alder, the son of Odin and Frigga, was beautiful, kind, and friendly.

He told his mother, Frigga, about the dream. Frigga was frightened. She worried that the dream was a sign of things to come. She loved her son and wanted to protect him. She went to Odin and told him about the dream.

"Is Balder in danger?" Frigga asked.

"I will look into it," Odin said.

Odin sent his two ravens out. They came back with alarming news.

"Hel, the goddess of the underworld, is making preparations," said one of the ravens.

"She is preparing to receive one of the gods in the kingdom of the dead," said the other.

Frigga begged Odin to send out his ravens to see if their son Balder was in danger.

"Which one?" asked Odin.

"That is more than we know," said the ravens.

When Frigga heard this, she decided to take action. She decided that she would talk to everything in the world and make each thing promise to do her son no **harm**.

Frigga went and spoke to the rocks.

"Rocks," she said, "promise me you will do no **harm** to my son, Balder."

"We will not fall on him," said the rocks. "We promise."

Frigga spoke to the water.

"Water," she said, "promise me you will do no **harm** to my son, Balder."

"I will not drown him," said the water. "I promise."

*igga decided to make everything in the world promise not to **harm** Balder.*

Frigga kept going. She spoke to all of the animals and made them promise to leave Balder alone. She spoke with the trees as well.

Loki knew what Frigga had done. He knew there was almost nothing that could **harm** Balder. Many times he had watched the gods play a game. They would throw rocks at Balder and watch the rocks bounce off. Sometimes they even shot arrows at him. The arrows broke into pieces and fell to the ground at Balder's feet. The gods laughed and laughed. But Loki did not laugh.

"There must be something that will not bounce off him," Loki said. "I will find out what it is."

Loki **disguised** himself as an old woman. He went to Frigga.

"Frigga," Loki said. "I have heard **rumors**. I have heard that your son Balder is in danger. I am a mother myself. I wanted to warn you, mother to mother."

rigga," Loki said. "I have heard **rumors**. I have heard that your son Balder is
danger."

"Thank you," said Frigga, "but you need not worry about Balder. I have spoken with everything that might **harm** him. I have made them all promise not to **harm** him."

"Has everything **sworn** to do him no **harm**?" Loki asked.

"Everything," said Frigga. "Well, almost everything. When I was talking to the oak tree, I spotted a little sprig of **mistletoe** growing on the oak. I was about to ask it to promise not to **harm** Balder, but I decided not to bother. What could **mistletoe** possibly do to anyone? It's such a tiny little plant! It hasn't even got roots of its own, you know. It grows on other trees and clings to them, as helpless as a baby clinging to its mother!"

"Yes," said Loki, "what could **mistletoe** do?"

But as he nodded his head in agreement, he was thinking, "**Mistletoe** will do much!"

*ʼe only thing that Frigga did not insist make a promise not to **harm** Balder was ʼistletoe.*

Chapter 7 The Death of Balder

Mistletoe was the only thing that had not sworn to protect Balder. When Loki found this out, he went and got a sprig of mistletoe. He cut the mistletoe into the shape of an arrow.

Then, he went to find Balder.

He found Balder and the other gods playing their favorite game. They were tossing things at Balder and laughing as they bounced away.

But there was one god who sat apart and did not join in the game. It was one of Balder's brothers, a god named Hod.

"Hod," said Loki, "why are you just sitting there? Why don't you join in the fun?"

"Loki," said Hod, "you know I'm blind. How can I throw things at Balder when I can't even see him?"

ki approached Hod with a sprig of mistletoe. Can you guess what Loki is up to?

"Here," said Loki, taking Hod by the hand. "I will help you. Place this arrow on the bow. I will point you in the right direction."

Loki guided Hod into position and told Hod to shoot the arrow. The sprig of mistletoe sped through the air, and, to everyone's amazement, struck Balder in the chest. Balder fell to the ground.

"What has happened?" cried Hod. "Did the arrow bounce off? Was it funny? What are you doing, brother? Are you playing at being dead?"

But Balder was not playing. He was really dead.

Loki smiled an evil smile. Then, he sneaked away.

When Frigga heard, she was in **despair**. She cried and raved.

"I will not let my son go to the underworld!" she swore. "I will not let Hel have him!"

"What happened?" cried Hod. "Did the arrow bounce off?"

The gods sent Hermod [HAER-m<u>oo</u>d], another of Balder's brothers, to talk to Hel, the goddess of the underworld. Odin loaned Hermod his eight-legged **steed**, Sleipner [SLEP-neer].

Hermod rode to the underworld.

Hel said that the gods could have Balder back—but only if every living thing in the world **mourned** for him.

Hermod mounted Sleipner and rode back to tell the gods.

Odin sent word: all things were to **mourn** for Balder.

Throughout all the halls of Asgard, the gods **mourned** for Balder.

Tyr went to Valhalla, where the bravest men from Earth feasted, waited upon by the Valkyries.

"Warriors!" Tyr called. "Valkyries! Hear me! Odin asks that you all join us in **mourning** for Balder."

All the men on Earth **mourned**. The animals **mourned**. The plants **mourned**, too.

*...din sent word: all things were to **mourn** for Balder.*

All things **mourned** for Balder—all except for Loki. He disguised himself as an old lady and appeared before Hermod.

"Good day, old lady," said Hermod. "I trust you will join us in weeping for Balder?"

"I will not," said Loki. "What do I care for Balder? Let Hel have him!"

That was it. The old lady had refused to **mourn** for Balder. Hel refused to let him return to the world of the living.

The gods placed Balder in a boat. Then, they set the boat on fire and shoved it out on the water.

As the flames rose into the sky, Frigga wept for the loss of her child. Her tears flowed freely, but tears would not bring Balder back. Nothing could bring him back.

*...ki, disguised as an old woman, refused to **mourn** for Balder.*

Chapter 8
Loki's Punishment

In time, the gods found out what Loki had done. They learned that it was Loki who had visited Frigga in disguise and found out about the mistletoe. It was Loki who had made the arrow and convinced blind Hod to shoot it at Balder. It was Loki, disguised as an old woman, who had refused to weep for Balder and kept him from returning to the land of the living.

Loki had been in trouble many times before. He had done all sorts of bad things. But he had never done anything quite so evil. The gods had lost all **patience** with him. Even Odin, who had defended Loki so many times in the past, refused to speak for him. The gods **vowed** to hunt him down and punish him.

Loki disguised himself as a salmon. He swam in the rivers. The gods tried to catch him but Loki leaped out of their nets and escaped. At last, Thor caught him. He grabbed him in midair. Loki struggled, but Thor held him tight with his powerful hands.

...ki disguised himself as a salmon. He struggled, but Thor held him tight with powerful hands.

The gods took Loki, who was no longer disguised as a salmon, to a cavern deep underground. They chained him to the rocks. They took a **serpent**, whose mouth dripped with poison, and fastened it to the roof. Drops of poison fell out of the **serpent's** mouth and landed on Loki.

Loki was in terrible pain. The poison dripped all night and all day and each drop stung like a knife **wound**. Loki, the giant who had lived in Asgard with the gods, **writhed** in **agony** on the floor of the cave.

Loki went on suffering until his wife Siguna heard about his troubles. Loki had treated Siguna badly, but she still loved him. She left Asgard and went to live with Loki in the cavern. She stood next to her husband, with a cup in her hand. She caught the drops of poison in the cup to keep them from falling on Loki. Loki still suffered, especially when Siguna had to empty the cup, but his suffering was much reduced.

...son dripped from the **serpent** all night and all day, causing Loki great pain.

As Loki lay in the cavern, Siguna whispered to him and soothed him. She reminded him of **prophecies** they both knew, **prophecies** about Ragnarok [ROG-no-rok] and the fall of the gods.

"For the moment, we are beaten," she said. "The gods in Asgard rejoice at their **triumph** over you. But they know that the day is coming. They have heard the **prophecies**. They know as well as you and I that the final battle, the battle of Ragnarok, is coming."

Siguna paused to toss a cup of poison away. Loki **writhed** in pain as two drops of poison fell on him. Siguna soothed him and began again.

ki's wife Siguna tried to catch the poison before it fell on him.

"When Ragnarok comes, Yggdrassil [EEG-dro-sil], the tree that holds up the world, will tremble. The giants will rise and fight against the gods. A great eagle with a white beak will shriek in the sky. Your son, Fenrir the Wolf, whom they keep chained in a cavern like this one, will break his chains and attack the gods themselves. He will swallow up Odin himself. Meanwhile, Jormungand [YOR-mun-gond], the mighty **serpent** whose body encircles the earth, will do battle with Thor—and Thor will not escape his **fate**. None of the gods will escape! All of them will die! The sun will turn black. Earth will sink into the sea. The stars will vanish. The world will be destroyed!"

When Ragnarok comes, the world will be destroyed.

Glossary for *Gods, Giants, and Dwarves*

A

adventure—an exciting or dangerous experience

agony—severe pain

anvil—a large, iron block used by blacksmiths on which heated metal is hit to shape it (**anvils**)

assembly—a meeting

awry—wrong, happening in an unexpected way

B

barrel-chested—having a large, round chest

beast—scoundrel

belch—to burp (**belched**)

boomerang—a curved stick that is thrown and then returns to the person who threw it

C

conceal—to hide (**concealed**)

corset—a tight, stiff undergarment worn to make a woman's waist appear smaller

craftsman—a person who is skilled in making things, especially by hand (**craftsmen**)

creature—a living thing, specifically an animal (**creatures**)

D

dainty—small and pretty, delicate

despair—a feeling of being hopeless or extremely sad

disguise—to hide by changing appearance (**disguised**)

dwarf—a mythical, human-like creature that lives underground (**dwarves**)

F

fast—does not eat for a period of time (**fasted**)

fate—the things that will happen to a person, destiny, fortune

flatter—to praise too much in a way that is not sincere or genuine (**flattered**, **flattery**)

forge—the furnace in a blacksmith shop used for heating metal

G

guardian—a person who watches and/or protects something or someone

H

harm—to hurt or damage someone or something

hideous—very ugly

J

journey—a trip

M

maid of honor—an unmarried female attendant of a bride

massive—huge

master—an expert (**masters**)

mead—a drink made by mixing water, honey, malt,

and yeast

mince words—to speak in an indirect and dishonest way

mistletoe—a plant with thick leaves and white berries; It grows on trees.

mourn—to feel or show sadness after a death or loss (**mourned**, **mourning**)

P

patience—able to put up with problems without getting upset

prophecy—a prediction of what will happen in the future (**prophecies**)

R

raven—a large, black bird that was one of many flying spies for Odin (**ravens**)

realm—a kingdom

rogue—a person who playfully causes trouble

rumor—a thing that people say to others about someone or something that may or may not be true (**rumors**)

S

scoundrel—a cruel, dishonest person

serpent—a snake

steed—a horse

summon—to call for (**summoned**)

surly—rude, mean, unfriendly

swear—to make a serious promise (**sworn**)

T

triumph—victory

V

veil—material worn on the head to cover the face

vein—a vessel like a tube that carries blood to the heart from other parts of the body (**veins**)

villainy—evil behavior

vow—to make an important and serious promise (**vowed**)

W

what a pity—that's too bad

wisdom—knowledge and good judgment gained over time

wound—an injury caused when something cuts or breaks the skin

writhe—to twist and turn in pain (**writhed**)

CORE KNOWLEDGE LANGUAGE ARTS

SERIES EDITOR-IN-CHIEF
E. D. Hirsch, Jr.

PRESIDENT
Linda Bevilacqua

⬤ORIAL STAFF

⬤olyn Gosse, Senior Editor - Preschool
⬤ara Turnbull, Materials Development Manager
⬤helle L. Warner, Senior Editor - Listening & Learning

⬤k Anderson
⬤in Blackshire
⬤ggie Buchanan
⬤la Coyner
⬤e Fulton
⬤a Hunt
⬤ Kist
⬤in Luecke
⬤ie McCormick
⬤thia Peng
⬤ Pettit
⬤n Sadler
⬤orah Samley
⬤ne Auger Smith
⬤ah Zelinke

DESIGN AND GRAPHICS STAFF

Scott Ritchie, Creative Director

Kim Berrall
Michael Donegan
Liza Greene
Matt Leech
Bridget Moriarty
Lauren Pack

CONSULTING PROJECT MANAGEMENT SERVICES

ScribeConcepts.com

ADDITIONAL CONSULTING SERVICES

Ang Blanchette
Dorrit Green
Carolyn Pinkerton

ACKNOWLEDGMENTS

⬤ materials are the result of the work, advice, and encouragement of numerous individuals over many years. Some of those singled out here already ⬤ the depth of our gratitude; others may be surprised to find themselves thanked publicly for help they gave quietly and generously for the sake of ⬤terprise alone. To helpers named and unnamed we are deeply grateful.

⬤TRIBUTORS TO EARLIER VERSIONS OF THESE MATERIALS

⬤ B. Albaugh, Kazuko Ashizawa, Nancy Braier, Kathryn M. Cummings, Michelle De Groot, Diana Espinal, Mary E. Forbes, Michael L. Ford, ⬤rsch, Danielle Knecht, James K. Lee, Diane Henry Leipzig, Martha G. Mack, Liana Mahoney, Isabel McLean, Steve Morrison, Juliane K. Munson, ⬤eth B. Rasmussen, Laura Tortorelli, Rachael L. Shaw, Sivan B. Sherman, Miriam E. Vidaver, Catherine S. Whittington, Jeannette A. Williams

⬤uld like to extend special recognition to Program Directors Matthew Davis and Souzanne Wright who were instrumental to the early ⬤opment of this program.

⬤OLS

⬤ truly grateful to the teachers, students, and administrators of the following schools for their willingness to field test these materials and for ⬤nvaluable advice: Capitol View Elementary, Challenge Foundation Academy (IN), Community Academy Public Charter School, Lake Lure Classical ⬤my, Lepanto Elementary School, New Holland Core Knowledge Academy, Paramount School of Excellence, Pioneer Challenge Foundation ⬤my, New York City PS 26R (The Carteret School), PS 30X (Wilton School), PS 50X (Clara Barton School), PS 96Q, PS 102X (Joseph O. Loretan), ⬤Q (The Bays Water), PS 214K (Michael Friedsam), PS 223Q (Lyndon B. Johnson School), PS 308K (Clara Cardwell), PS 333Q (Goldie Maple Academy), ⬤yah Elementary School, South Shore Charter Public School, Spartanburg Charter School, Steed Elementary School, Thomas Jefferson Classical ⬤my, Three Oaks Elementary, West Manor Elementary.

⬤special thanks to the CKLA Pilot Coordinators Anita Henderson, Yasmin Lugo-Hernandez, and Susan Smith, whose suggestions and day-to-day ⬤rt to teachers using these materials in their classrooms was critical.

CREDITS

EXPERT REVIEWER
Andrew McDonald

WRITERS
Matt Davis

ILLUSTRATORS AND IMAGE SOURCES
All illustrations by Brittany Tingey